POSITIVE ATTITUDE

POSITIVE ATTITUDE

by SCOTT ADAMS

Andrews McMeel
Publishing®

Kansas City • Sydney • London

Andrews McMeel Publishing, LLC
an Andrews McMeel Universal company
1130 Walnut Street, Kansas City, Missouri 64106

www.andrewsmcmeel.com
www.dilbert.com

15 16 17 18 19 SDB 10 9 8 7 6 5 4 3 2 1

ISBN: 978-1-4494-7084-5

—— **ATTENTION: SCHOOLS AND BUSINESSES** ——

Andrews McMeel books are available at quantity discounts with bulk purchase for educational, business, or sales promotional use. For information, please e-mail the Andrews McMeel Publishing Special Sales Department: specialsales@amuniversal.com.

Recent DILBERT® Books from Andrews McMeel Publishing

I Sense a Coldness to Your Mentoring
ISBN: 978-1-4494-2938-6

Your New Job Title Is "Accomplice"
ISBN: 978-1-4494-2775-7

I Can't Remember If We're Cheap or Smart
ISBN: 978-1-4494-2309-4

Teamwork Means You Can't Pick the Side that's Right
ISBN: 978-1-4494-1018-6

How's That Underling Thing Working Out for You?
ISBN: 978-1-4494-0819-0

Your Accomplishments Are Suspiciously Hard to Verify
ISBN: 978-1-4494-0102-3

Problem Identified and You're Probably Not Part of the Solution
ISBN: 978-0-7407-8534-4

I'm Tempted to Stop Acting Randomly
ISBN: 978-0-7407-7806-3

14 Years of Loyal Service in a Fabric-Covered Box
ISBN: 978-0-7407-7365-5

Freedom's Just Another Word for People Finding Out You're Useless
ISBN: 978-0-7407-7815-5

Dilbert 2.0: 20 Years of Dilbert
ISBN: 978-0-7407-7735-6

This Is the Part Where You Pretend to Add Value
ISBN: 978-0-7407-7227-6

Introduction

There's a big difference between optimism and insanity. An insane person keeps doing the same thing over and over again expecting a different result. An optimist does that, too, but he doesn't know he's doing the same thing over and over. For example, an optimist might go to work every day and imagine that today's series of meetings will be the ones that fix all of the problems caused by yesterday's series of meetings. Optimists believe that's totally different from insanity, because the meetings are not in the same room every time.

I understand optimists because I am one. When I began my corporate career, I expected that my hard work and talent would be rewarded, despite all evidence to the contrary. I came to work every day, sat in my fabric-covered box, and expected something terrific to happen at any minute. I had a positive attitude that was, again, totally different from insanity.

Every time my corporate employer announced a new round of downsizing, my first thought was that it would soon be easier to find parking. When I worked on a project for a year only to have it canceled for budget reasons, I was happy because it freed my schedule so I could—if I were lucky—go fail at something more interesting.

Eventually I became a cartoonist. But I imbued Dilbert with my irrationally positive workplace attitude. He carries on in my tradition, showing up for work every day and expecting some good to come of it.

Speaking of good things, there's still time to join Dogbert's New Ruling Class. Just sign up for the free *Dilbert Newsletter* that is published approximately whenever I feel like it. To sign up, go to www.dilbert.com and follow the subscription instructions.

S.Adams

Scott Adams

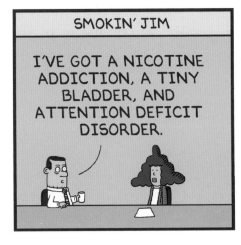

STINKY PETE

I WAS JOGGING TO WORK AND EATING MY ONION SANDWICH WHEN I SPOTTED A SEWAGE SPILL.

SO I DID WHAT ANY—ONE WOULD DO IN THAT SITUATION: I ROLLED AROUND IN IT.

A PENNY FOR YOUR THOUGHTS.

I MUST INSERT MY HEAD INTO MY BUTTOCKS SO I CAN BREATHE.

I CAN NO LONGER WORK WITH YOU BECAUSE OF WHAT YOU SAID TO SOMEONE ABOUT ME.

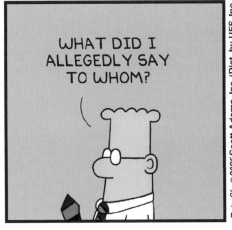

WHAT DID I ALLEGEDLY SAY TO WHOM?

I CAN'T TELL YOU WITHOUT VIOLATING THE INSANE CHICK CODE OF ETHICS.

WELCOME TO THE MONTHLY MEETING OF INSANE CHICKS.

OUR SPEAKER TODAY IS BETTY, AND HER TOPIC IS "ALL THE PEOPLE WHO ARE INTENTIONALLY HURTING US."

THE BREAKOUT SESSION IS TITLED "HOW TO TURN YOUR IMAGINARY PROBLEMS INTO REAL ONES."

THE SOCIETY OF
INSANE CHICKS

I KNOW HE HATES ME BECAUSE HE LIKES TO PLAY RACQUETBALL.

MAYBE HE JUST LIKES RACQUETBALL. AND WANTS TO STAY HEALTHY.

LEAVE NOW.

I DID A BACK— GROUND CHECK AND DISCOVERED THAT YOU EMBELLISHED YOUR RÉSUMÉ.

FOR EXAMPLE, THERE'S NO COLLEGE NAMED "THE EINSTEIN ONE."

AND I'M REASON— ABLY CERTAIN THAT "SMARTOLOGY" ISN'T A REAL MAJOR.

NOW THAT I KNOW YOUR RÉSUMÉ WAS EMBELLISHED, YOU NEED TO TALK TO THE VP OF HUMAN RESOURCES.

ARE YOU GOING TO FIRE ME?

NAH. I'LL LET YOU IN ON A LITTLE SECRET.

I'M THE FICUS TREE THAT USED TO BE IN THE LOBBY.

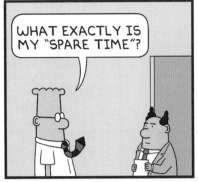

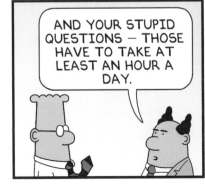

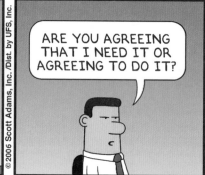

WALLY, ARE YOU SURE YOU SHOULD EAT THAT BURRITO? YOU DO NOT HAVE ISO 9004-3 CERTI- FICATION.

HA HA HA HA HA HA HA HA HA HA

IT IS ENTIRELY POSSIBLE THAT I HAVE BEEN WORKING HERE FOR TOO LONG.

IS IT MORE IMPORTANT TO FOLLOW OUR DOCU- MENTED PROCESS OR TO MEET THE DEADLINE?

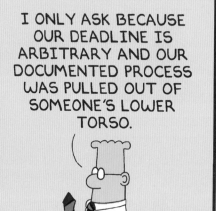

I ONLY ASK BECAUSE OUR DEADLINE IS ARBITRARY AND OUR DOCUMENTED PROCESS WAS PULLED OUT OF SOMEONE'S LOWER TORSO.

WHERE'S YOUR ARTIFICIAL SENSE OF URGENCY?

TEAM- WORK KILLED IT.

WALLY, I CAME TO ASK YOU FOR THE NEW DESIGN SPECS.

BUT WE BOTH KNOW YOU'LL SEND ME TO SOMEONE WHO DOESN'T HAVE THEM. AND THAT PERSON WILL REFER ME BACK TO YOU.

WHEN I RETURN, YOU WILL HAVE ESCAPED TO YOUR SECRET HIDING PLACE.

TED HAS THE SPECS.

I'M LIKE THE STORY OF THE AUTO MECHANIC.

A WOMAN HAS HER CAR TOWED INTO THE SHOP. THE MECHANIC OPENS THE HOOD AND TAKES A LOOK.

AFTER ABOUT TEN SECONDS HE TAKES A HAMMER AND TAPS THE ENGINE. IT STARTS RIGHT UP.

THE MECHANIC SAYS, "THAT WILL BE $100, PLEASE."

ZZZZ

THE WOMAN SAYS, "$100??? ALL YOU DID WAS TAP THE ENGINE!"

THE MECHANIC SAYS, "IT'S $90 FOR KNOWING WHERE TO TAP AND $10 FOR THE TAP."

ZZZZZ

TAP!

20 YEARS AGO I WOULDN'T HAVE KNOWN WHICH ONE OF YOU TO TAP.

38

39

THE HIGHLIGHT OF MY WORKDAY IS THIS HAM SANDWICH.

FROM NOW UNTIL QUITTING TIME, NOTHING ELSE WILL BE AS REWARDING.

WHAT DO YOU DO AFTER WORK?

I THINK ABOUT THE SANDWICH.

WE CAN KICK A FIELD GOAL IN THE NINTH INNING IF WE USE A FULL-COURT PRESS.

REMEMBER THAT YOU DRIVE FOR SHOW BUT YOU PICK UP THE SPARE FOR DOUGH.

HAVE YOU BEEN HELP-ING ALICE WITH HER SPORTS METAPHORS?

PERHAPS.

EXECUTIVE COMPENSATION REVIEW BOARD

HOW MUCH SHOULD WE PAY OUR CEO IF HE JUST SHOWS UP FOR WORK?

FIFTY MILLION DOLLARS!!!

HONK HONK

THE CLOWN MAKES A GOOD ARGUMENT.

AYE!

THE ENEMY WAS LESS THAN FIFTY FEET AWAY AND MY ONLY HOPE WAS TO CALL FOR AN AIR STRIKE.

THAT REMINDS ME OF THE TIME I RAN OUT OF STAPLES AND HAD TO USE GLUE.

AND THEN A SNIPER SPOTTED ME.

MY GLUE WAS BAD.

STEVE, ASK EVERYONE IN THE DEPARTMENT TO SIGN THIS BIRTHDAY CARD FOR MY SECRETARY.

I'VE LED MEN IN COMBAT AND THIS IS THE SORT OF ASSIGNMENT YOU GIVE ME???

ALSO, RUN DOWN TO THE CONVENIENCE STORE AND BUY HER SOMETHING FLUFFY OR ORANGE.

WHAT ARE YOU GOING TO WEAR TO TED'S WEDDING?

WHATEVER COMES UP IN THE ROTATION.

THEN SHE SHRIEKED SOME NONSENSE ABOUT SPENDING SIX MONTHS SHOPPING FOR SHOES AND STARTED TO PUNCH ME.

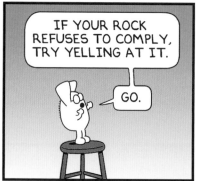

© 2006 Scott Adams, Inc. /Dist. by UFS, Inc.

10-11-06

53

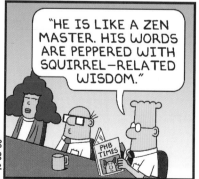

© 2006 Scott Adams, Inc./Dist. by UFS, Inc.

10-08-06

57

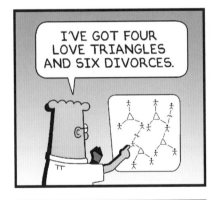

60

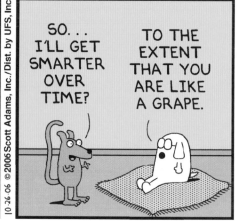

TODAY I WILL TEACH YOU HOW TO USE YOUR INCOMPETENCE TO ACHIEVE YOUR GOALS.

STEP 1: BE INCOMPETENT. (ALSO KNOWN AS "THE EASY PART.")

STEP 2: VOLUNTEER FOR THE MOST DIFFICULT AND IMPORTANT PROJECTS

STEP 3: CONVINCE YOUR BOSS THAT AN ENEMY WITHIN THE COMPANY IS SLOWING YOU DOWN.

STEP 4: INSIST THAT COMPETENT PEOPLE BE PULLED OFF OF OTHER PROJECTS TO HELP YOU.

STEP 5: DECLARE YOUR-SELF THE LEADER OF THE COMPETENT PEOPLE

STEP 6: CLAIM CREDIT FOR THE WORK OF THE COMPETENT PEOPLE.

STEP 7: AFTER YOU GET PROMOTED, FIRE THE COMPETENT PEOPLE TO ELIMINATE WITNESSES.

© 2006 Scott Adams, Inc. /Dist. by UFS, Inc.

11-05-06

68

WE'VE GOT A DEAD GUY IN CUBICLE D-32.

UH-OH.

DO YOU HAVE ANY IDEA HOW MUCH PAPERWORK IT CAUSES WHEN SOME- ONE DIES IN ONE OF MY CUBICLES?

TEN MORE FEET TO THE MARKETING DEPARTMENT.

11-9-06

GET THE USER DATA FROM ED.

THAT'S IMPOS- SIBLE.

ED IS AN UNREACHABLE. HE DOESN'T ANSWER HIS PHONE OR RETURN MESSAGES. HE'S NEVER IN HIS CUBICLE AND HE DOESN'T READ E-MAIL.

DOES HE USE THE REST- ROOM?

NO, WE THINK HE MODIFIED HIS BRIEF- CASE.

11-10-06

I NEED SOME DATA FROM AN UNREACHABLE GUY NAMED ED. WHAT SHOULD I DO?

JUST MAKE UP A BUNCH OF DATA LIKE EVERYONE ELSE DOES.

EVERY- ONE ELSE DOES THAT?

ARE YOU DOUBTING MY DATA?

11-11-06

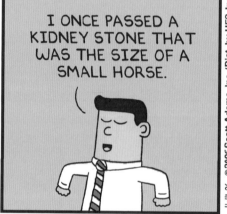

73

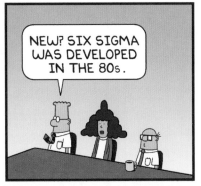

DID YOU TELL ASOK TO GET OUR CLIENT A "LITTLE BIT PREGNANT"?

YES.

WELL, HE DOESN'T UNDERSTAND ALL OF OUR AMERICAN SAYINGS.

I DON'T KNOW WHAT THIS IS ALL ABOUT, BUT I'M IN.

I'VE BEEN TRYING FOR SIX MONTHS TO SOLVE THIS ENGINEERING PROBLEM. IT MIGHT BE IMPOSSIBLE.

JUST TURN IT SIDEWAYS AND IT WILL FIT PERFECTLY.

OKAY... NOW I HAVE TO KILL YOU.

WE MIGHT NEED TO RESTATE OUR EARNINGS.

IT TURNS OUT THAT WE'RE NOT ALLOWED TO MAKE UP NUMBERS.

DID YOU KNOW THAT "FRILLION" ISN'T AN ACTUAL NUMBER?

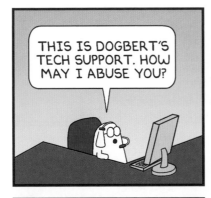

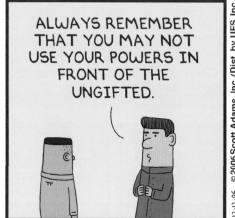

84

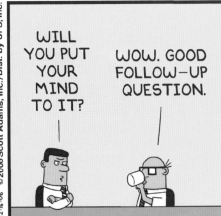

85

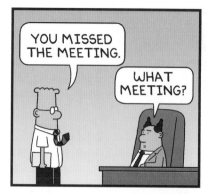

BOB, THE UNLUCKIEST INSURANCE AGENT.

OUR HAZARD COVERAGE IS SECOND TO NONE!

DON'T FLEE DOWN THE STAIRWELL. THE STEPS ARE MADE OF ASBESTOS.

THERE'S AN ARTICLE IN THE PAPER ABOUT THAT GUY YOU VOTED FOR.

HE'S HAVING AN AFFAIR WITH A SQUIRREL.

WANT TO TALK POLITICS?

SHUT UP.

I HEARD THAT THE GUY YOU VOTED FOR JUST CONFESSED TO HAVING AN AFFAIR WITH A SQUIRREL.

SHUT UP. THE GUY YOU VOTED FOR IS BEING SUED FOR CHOKING HIS SECRETARY.

IN SOME COUNTRIES THEY DON'T GET A CHOICE OF WHO TO VOTE FOR.

I FEEL SORRY FOR THEM.

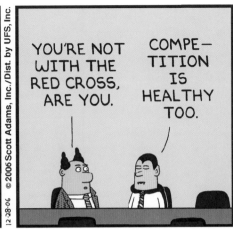

I'M MAKING YOU A SALES ENGINEER. YOU'LL BE PAID ON COMMISSION.

WHEN OUR SALES REPS LIE, IT WILL BE YOUR JOB TO MAKE IT LOOK LIKE THE TRUTH.

TRY TO AVOID FACTS.

© 2007 Scott Adams, Inc./Dist. by UFS, Inc. 1-8-07

SALES ENGINEER

YOUR SALES REP TOLD US THAT THE PRODUCT HEALS ITSELF. IS THAT TRUE?

IT'S TOTALLY TRUE... THAT HE SAID THAT.

LET ME ASK THIS ANOTHER WAY...

NOOO!!! ONE WAY PER QUESTION!

© 2007 Scott Adams, Inc./Dist. by UFS, Inc. 1-9-07

I'M A SALES SUPPORT ENGINEER NOW. CAN YOU TEACH ME TO BE A GOOD LIAR?

SURE. MEET ME ON THE PORCH, AND DON'T WEAR A COAT; THE COLD WILL HELP THE LEARNING.

THE FIRST LESSON IS ALWAYS THE CRUELEST.

© 2007 Scott Adams, Inc./Dist. by UFS, Inc. 1-10-07

SALES ENGINEER

I DID THE HARD PART OF MAKING THE SALE. ALL YOU HAVE TO DO IS INSTALL IT.

I MIGHT HAVE PROMISED THEM A FEW EXTRA FEATURES.

DID YOU BRING YOUR OWN MASSAGE TABLE OR SHOULD I JUST GET NAKED AND SPRAWL ON A DESK?

YOUR NETWORK PRODUCT APPEARS TO BE A SHOEBOX FULL OF TWIGS AND LEAVES.

HO HO! JUST WAIT UNTIL MY ENGINEER DOES HIS MAGIC AND INTEGRATES IT WITH YOUR NETWORK!

MAKE IT LOOK LIKE ANOTHER VENDOR'S FAULT.

SALES ENGINEER

I'VE SUCCESSFULLY INTEGRATED OUR PRODUCT WITH YOUR NETWORK.

IT MIGHT LOOK AS IF ALL I DID WAS RUN A CAT5 CABLE THROUGH A SHOEBOX FULL OF TWIGS AND LEAVES.

IS THAT ALL YOU DID?

A CAT6 CABLE WOULD BE OVERKILL.

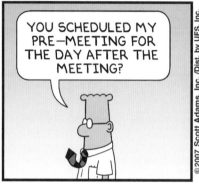

TRA-LA-LA LA-LA-LA-LA!!!

WHY DO I NEED A REASON?

EVERY WEEK I ORDER SUGARED DOUGHNUTS ONLINE AND EVERY WEEK THEY DELIVER PLAIN DOUGHNUTS.

THOSE AREN'T PLAIN. RATBERT LICKS THE SUGAR OFF OF THEM WHEN THEY ARRIVE.

I WORK IN A CUBICLE. I CAN GET USED TO THIS TOO.

DOGBERT'S PASSWORD RECOVERY SERVICE FOR MORONS

I DON'T REMEMBER MY PASSWORD.

IS IT "123"?

THAT'S JUST SPOOKY.

CATBERT: EVIL DIRECTOR OF HUMAN RESOURCES

I AM A SCIENTIST FROM THE PLANET ZORP. I BRING YOU TECHNOLOGIES BEYOND YOUR IMAGINATION.

ALL I ASK IS THAT YOU LET ME WORK WITH YOUR ENGINEERS TO TRANSFER THIS KNOWLEDGE.

THEY THINK "WORK" MEANS SITTING IN A FABRIC-COVERED CONTAINER.

I AM AN ALIEN WITH HIGHLY ADVANCED INTELLIGENCE. I HAVE COME TO SHARE MY GENIUS WITH THIS COMPANY.

ME TOO. BUT THEY DON'T LIKE THAT SORT OF THING HERE.

IT'S A QUAGMIRE.

I CAME TO THIS COMPANY TO BRING THE TECHNOLOGY OF MY ADVANCED CULTURE TO YOU SIMPLETONS.

HAS ANYONE EVER TOLD YOU THAT YOUR SNOUT IS LIKE THE HANDLE OF A GAVEL?

A WHAT?

HOW'S THE NEW GUY WORKING OUT?

ORDER IN THE COURT!

BAM BAM BAM

I CAME FROM A DISTANT PLANET TO BRING YOU ADVANCED TECHNOLOGY, BUT NO ONE HERE WILL LISTEN!

I AM A SUPERIOR BEING, YOU MORON! LISTEN TO WHAT I TELL YOU AND THEN DO IT!

I FIRED HIM BEFORE HE STARTED YAMMERING ABOUT LINUX.

EASY COME, EASY GO.

CAN YOU COME TO A MEETING RIGHT NOW?

NO, IT'S ALMOST LUNCH TIME.

IF I MISS LUNCH, MY DAY WILL BE 12 HOURS OF UNINTER— RUPTED MISERY. I WILL ENVY THE DEAD.

THAT'S STUPID. THE DEAD DON'T EAT LUNCH EITHER.

ASOK, YOUR ASSIGN— MENT IS TO BUY A DISPLAY CASE FOR OUR AWARDS.

THEN GO TO THE AWARDS STORE AND BUY A BUNCH OF AWARDS BECAUSE WE DON'T HAVE ANY.

THE NEXT ONE IS FOR "BEST UNETHICAL FILLING OF AN AWARDS SHOWCASE."

104

104

© 2007 Scott Adams, Inc. /Dist. by UFS, Inc.

109

OUR TRAVEL BUDGET IS SHOT.

WE'LL TAKE MONEY OUT OF THE TRAINING BUDGET.

WE NEED TRAINING TO SUPPORT OUR NEW PRODUCT.

WE'LL USE THE SOFTWARE BUDGET FOR TRAINING.

WE NEED TO DO A MANDATORY SOFTWARE UPGRADE.

FINE. MOVE SOME MONEY FROM THE TRAVEL BUDGET TO THE SOFTWARE BUDGET.

GEEZ, YOU PEOPLE DO NOTHING BUT COMPLAIN. MEANWHILE I'M MANAGING MY BRAINS OUT.

I WONDERED WHAT HAPPENED TO THEM.

HAPPENED TO WHAT?

CATBERT: EVIL DIRECTOR OF HUMAN RESOURCES

THE NEW COMPANY HEALTH PLAN IS GOOGLE.

FROM NOW ON, EMPLOYEES MUST USE GOOGLE TO DIAGNOSE THEIR OWN ILLNESSES.

FOR EXAMPLE, THIS GUY HAS A GROWTH ON HIS NECK.

I DO?

A QUICK SEARCH ON MY BLACKBERRY TELLS ME IT'S...

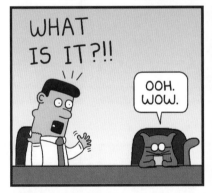

WHAT IS IT?!!

OOH. WOW.

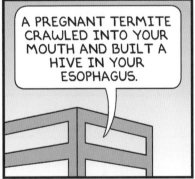

A PREGNANT TERMITE CRAWLED INTO YOUR MOUTH AND BUILT A HIVE IN YOUR ESOPHAGUS.

GAAA!!!

STOP BEING A BABY.

THE TREATMENT FOR THAT IS...

DO YOU HAVE AN ARC WELDER AND A BARREL OF KEROSENE?

113

I HIRED THE DOGBERT PUBLIC RELATIONS FIRM TO GET US SOME FREE PUBLICITY.

I'VE ALREADY TOLD THE MEDIA THAT YOUR PRODUCTS ARE DEADLY AND WE'RE VOLUNTARILY RECALLING EVERYTHING.

BUT... THEY AREN'T DEADLY.

HEY, I DON'T TELL YOU HOW TO BE FAT.

SNORK

DOGBERT DOES PUBLIC RELATIONS

OUR PRODUCTS ARE MADE BY ASTHMATIC DWARVES. YOU SHOULD DO A STORY ON THAT.

NOT ENOUGH? OKAY, WHAT IF THE DWARVES ARE ALSO POLYGAMOUS SERIAL KILLERS?

WHEN YOU TALK TO THE REPORTER, TRY TO SLOUCH, WHEEZE, AND ACT HENPECKED TO THE POINT OF HOMICIDE.

DOGBERT DOES PUBLIC RELATIONS

YOU CAN'T GET FREE PUBLICITY SIMPLY BY DOING SOMETHING BETTER.

YOU HAVE TO DO SOMETHING IN A WAY THAT HAS NEVER BEEN DONE.

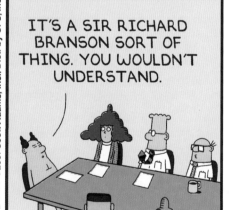

IT'S A SIR RICHARD BRANSON SORT OF THING. YOU WOULDN'T UNDERSTAND.

THE FACILITIES PEOPLE TELL ME THERE'S ASBESTOS IN THE CEILING.

THEY SAY YOU DON'T NEED TO WORRY ABOUT IT UNLESS IT GETS DISTURBED.

THEY PLAN TO DISTURB IT TODAY.

THE EMPLOYEES ARE GETTING ALL WHINEY ABOUT THE ASBESTOS IN THE CEILING.

I TOLD THEM IT WASN'T DANGEROUS, BUT APPARENTLY I'M NOT CREDIBLE IN THIS HAZMAT SUIT.

I DON'T THINK IT'S FAIR THAT THEY JUDGE ME BY MY CLOTHES.

THEY FOUND ASBESTOS IN OUR CEILING. WE'RE ALL IN DANGER.

I MUST USE MY TELEKINESIS TO REMOVE THE ASBESTOS.

GAAA!

THE THREAT HAS BEEN NEUTRALIZED. YOU MUST NEVER ASK ME HOW IT WAS DONE.

I'M NOT EVEN CURIOUS.

118

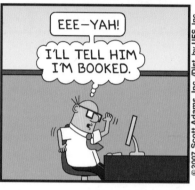